Contents

English

We're on Our Way! 

Help the Romeros and their friends get to the zoo.
Look at the names of places they will pass.
Number the words in alphabetical order.
Then follow the path from 1 to 8.

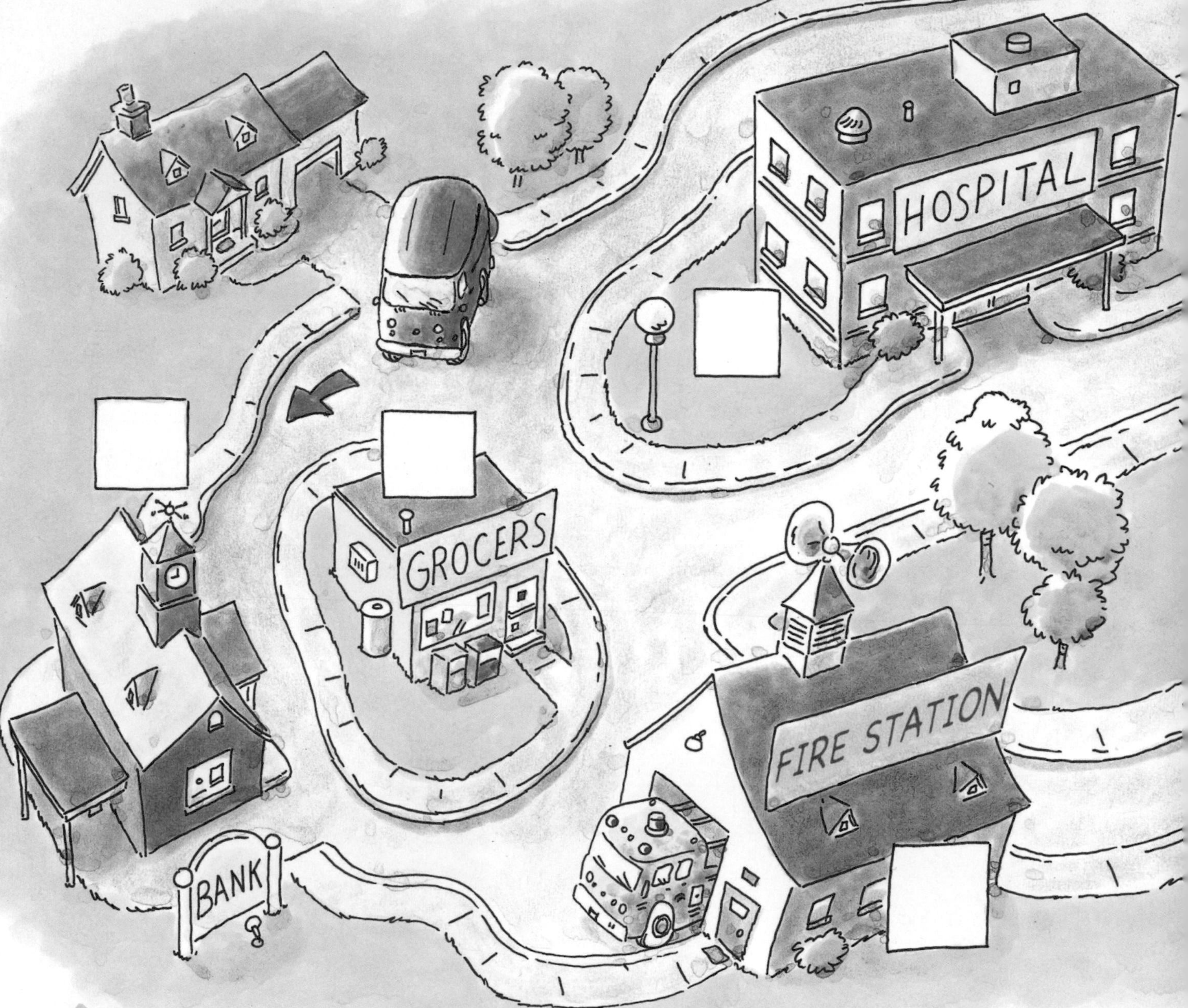

HOSPITAL

GROCERS

FIRE STATION

BANK

Try This!

Draw a map. Show how to get from your house to a favourite place. Show the roads on which you travel. Include the places you pass.

POST OFFICE
SCHOOL
TOYS
ZIPPITY ZOO
Ha! Ha! Ha!
Which animal knows its alphabet?
The alpha-bat!

What's Up at the Zoo?

Look at the zoo map and the map key.
Then follow the directions.

ZIPPITY ZOO

1. Draw a line to show a way to the Snake House.

2. Draw a □ to show where you can see a [tiger].

3. Draw a △ to show where you can see a [duck].

Write the name of the place you would go first.

4. 

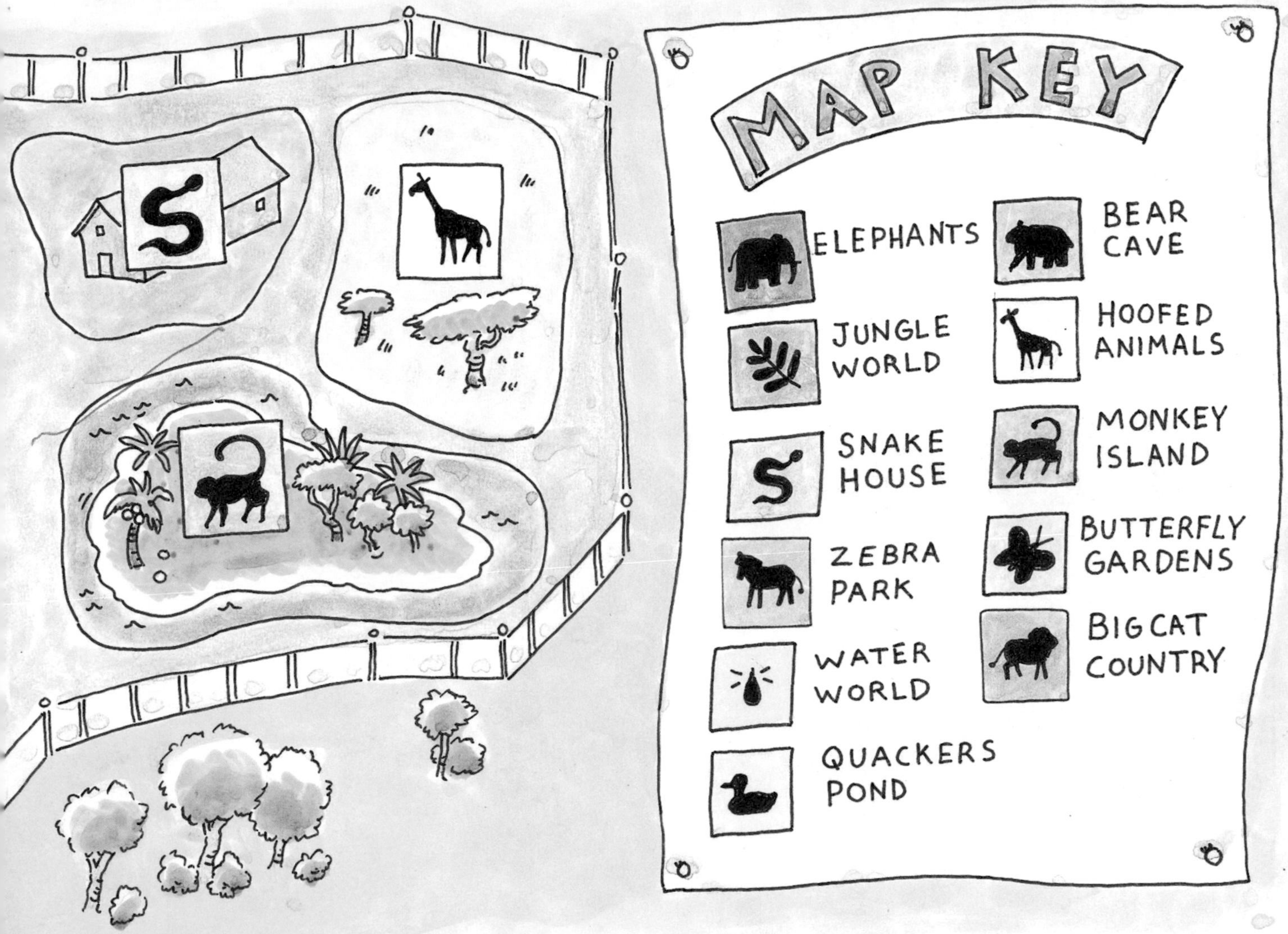

MAP KEY
ELEPHANTS
BEAR CAVE
JUNGLE WORLD
HOOFED ANIMALS
SNAKE HOUSE
MONKEY ISLAND
ZEBRA PARK
BUTTERFLY GARDENS
WATER WORLD
BIG CAT COUNTRY
QUACKERS POND

Write **yes** or **no**.

5. Can you see an in the zoo? yes yes

6. Can you see a in the zoo?

7. Can you see a in the zoo? no

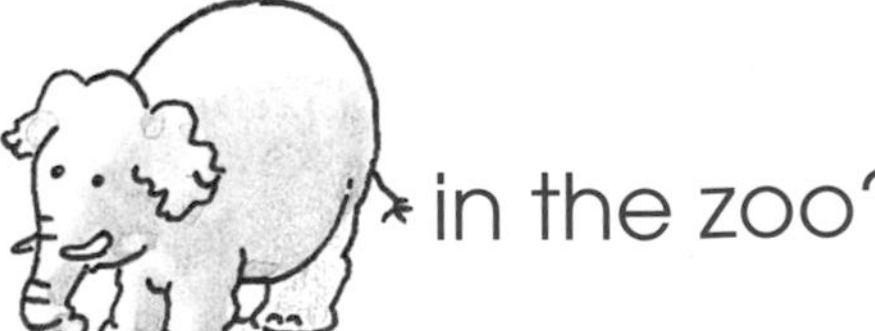

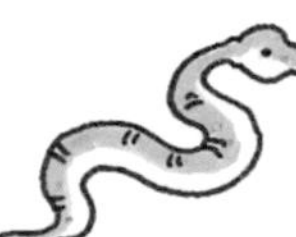

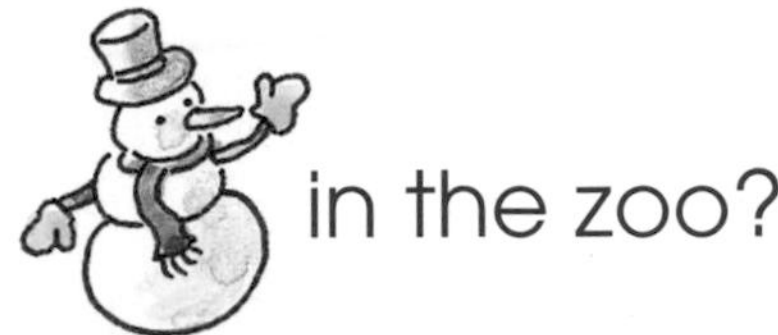

Puzzling Names

Write the first letter of each picture.
Read the animal name.
Write the number in its circle.

1. ____ ____ ____ ____

2. ____ ____ ____ ____ ____ ____

3. ____ ____ ____ ____ ____

Try This!

Make a puzzle! You need nature magazines to cut up, scissors, glue and heavy paper or cardboard.

1. Cut out a large picture of an animal.
2. Glue the picture on cardboard or heavy paper.
3. Cut the picture into puzzle pieces.
4. Put your puzzle back together.

Water World

Say **a, e, i, o** and **u**. These are the long vowels.
Then say the words on the fish.
Colour the long vowel fish **orange**.

The other words have short vowel sounds.
Colour the short vowel fish **green**.

Help the squid get to her cave.
Draw a line to connect the long vowel fish.

Honey Bear

Honey Bear is running in circles!
She is looking for words with short vowel sounds.
Start at the arrow. Write eight words you find.
Then go the other way. Say the words.

Have an adult help you make this honey of a treat.

- 2 apples, cored & peeled
- 1/2 cup raisins
- 1 tablespoon honey
- 1/2 cup walnut pieces
- 1/4 cup apple juice
- 8 crackers

1. Chop the apples, walnuts and raisins.
2. Stir in the juice and honey.
3. Spread on crackers. Eat!

A Cool Rhyme

Read the rhyme.
Then draw a line under each number word.

Penguin Pals

Five little penguin pals resting on the shore
One took a dip, and then there were four
Four little penguin pals walking by the sea
One little slip, and then there were three
Three little penguin pals with nothing to do
One little trip, and then there were two
Two little penguin pals looking for fun
One little flip, and then there was one
One little penguin all alone
He jumped in too, and now there are none!

Write the words that rhyme with **tip**.
Say other words that rhyme with **tip**.

1. ______________________ 2. ______________________

3. ______________________ 4. ______________________

Quackers Pond

Look at the pond. Write how many of each.

1. ____________

2. ____________

3. ____________

4. ____________

5. ____________

6. ____________

7. Draw 10 in the pond.

Sneaky Snakes

Write an **s** blend to finish each picture name. Choose from these.

1. ______ ake
2. ______ an
3. ______ ider
4. ______ unk
5. ______ ug
6. ______ arfish

Circle words with **s** blends in the puzzle.

x	b	s	k	u	n	k
v	s	t	o	p	s	g
s	w	a	n	g	n	s
f	t	r	y	c	o	l
t	u	f	z	j	w	u
s	p	i	d	e	r	g
y	o	s	n	a	k	e
p	q	h	s	n	a	p

Try This!

Play a blend game. You need six paper cups and a pen. Label each cup with one blend: sn, sl, st, sp, sw, sk. Line up the cups on a table. Toss a soft ball or beanbag toy at the cups. For each cup you knock over, say a word that begins with the blend.

Desert Trail

Follow the path through the desert.
Add numerals to write the **totals**.
Subtract numerals to write the **differences**.

Where Are the Animals?

Where are the animals on the Desert Trail?
Finish each sentence with a word below.

over under in across on

1. The roadrunner  runs ______________ the .

2. The lizard  sleeps ______________ the 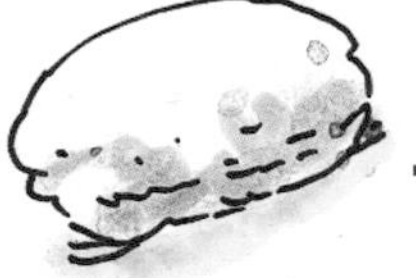.

3. The jack rabbit  leaps ______________ the .

4. The snake  glides ______________ the .

5. The owl  sits ______________ the 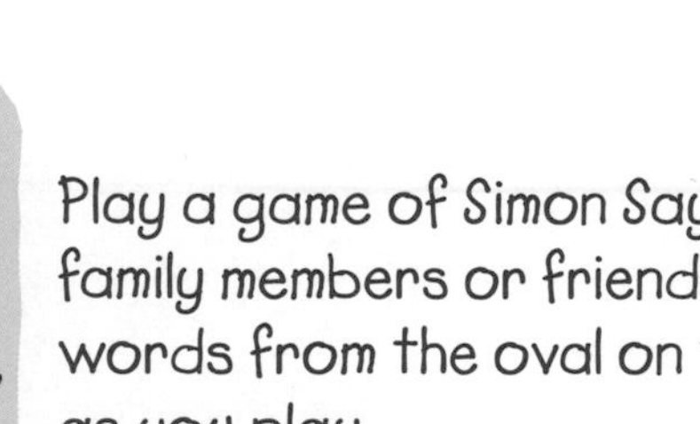.

Try This!

Play a game of Simon Says with family members or friends. Use the words from the oval on this page as you play.

We Work at the Zoo

Here are four people who work at Zippity Zoo.
Circle the name in each sentence.

Remember – a person's name begins with a capital letter.

Jan helps sick animals. Bob keeps animal homes clean.

Chan teaches sea animals. Lisa feeds hungry animals.

Write the correct name under each picture.

1. ____________________

2. ____________________

3. ____________________

4. ____________________

Try This!

To make dough names, you need 1 cup peanut butter, 1 cup honey and 2 cups powdered milk.

1. Wash your hands.
2. Mix the ingredients in a bowl.
3. Add more milk if the dough is too sticky.
4. Form the dough into the letters of your name.
5. Eat your name!

The names of special places begin with capital letters.
Zippity Zoo is a special place.
Zippity and **Zoo** begin with capital letters.
Circle the name of the special place in each sentence.

1. Parrots live in Jungle World.

2. Ducks swim in Quackers Pond.

3. Deer run in Zebra Park.

4. Monkeys make noise on Monkey Island.

Look back at pages 4 and 5. Write the name of the special place bears live.

Big Cat Country

A word can name one.  **lion**

A word can name more than one.   **lions**

Many words add **s** to name more than one.

Write a number sentence about each picture.
Add **s** to make the name of each kind of cat mean more than one.

____

\+ ____

= ____ tiger ____.

____

\+ ____

= ____ leopard ____.

____

\+ ____

= ____ bobcat ____.

____

\+ ____

= ____ lion ____.

Disappearing Animals

Cut out the book and put it together.
Write number sentences.
Tell the story in your own words.

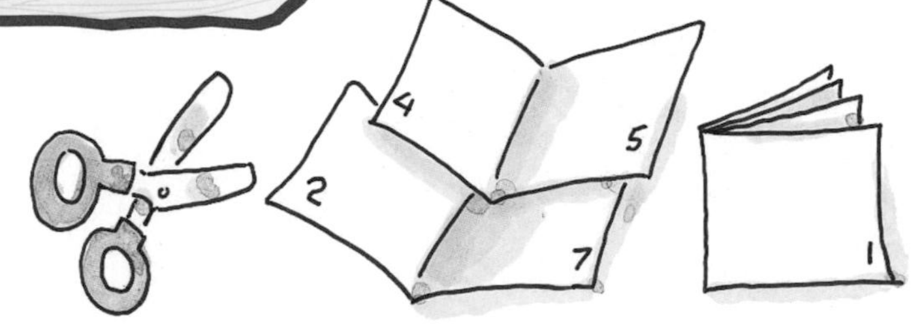

___ − ___ = ___

8

Captain Croc's Zippity-Zoo Riverboat by

___

Captain Croc has a riverboat. Animals like to ride in his boat. Here come some now! Turn the page to begin the story.

1

___ + ___ = ___

6

___ − ___ = ___

3

Try This!

Make number sentences using dominoes.
You need a set of dominoes, paper and a pencil.
Look at the number of dots on both halves of a domino. Write a number sentence to show how many dots altogether.

4 + 3 = 7

2 + 6 = 8

Disappearing Animals

What did the maths book say to the storybook?

I've got a lot of problems!

Ha! Ha! Ha!

___ + ___ = ___ 2

___ − ___ = ___ 7

___ + ___ = ___ 4

___ − ___ = ___ 5

Try This!

1	2	3	4
5	6	7	8
9	10	11	12

Make this game board. You need a large piece of paper, chalk and coins, buttons or stones. Use the chalk to make the game board inside on the paper or outside on the pavement. Toss two coins or buttons on a paper game board or two stones on a large chalk game board. Subtract the smaller number from the larger number.

Play Like the Animals 

Action words tell what people and animals do.
Under each picture, write an action word from the oval.
Then draw lines to match the children with the animals doing the same actions.

climb dig **slide** jump

1. ____________

2. ____________

3. ____________

4. ____________

Baby Talk

Some baby animals have names that are different from their parents. A baby pig is a **piglet**. What is a baby cat?

Draw a line from each baby to its parent.

Write a baby animal name to finish each sentence.

1. **Seal** goes with ________________. 2. **Tiger** goes with ________________.

Let Me Out!

fish snake
chick robin

Some animals hatch from eggs.
Look at these eggs.
Write the name of each animal.

I sing in spring!

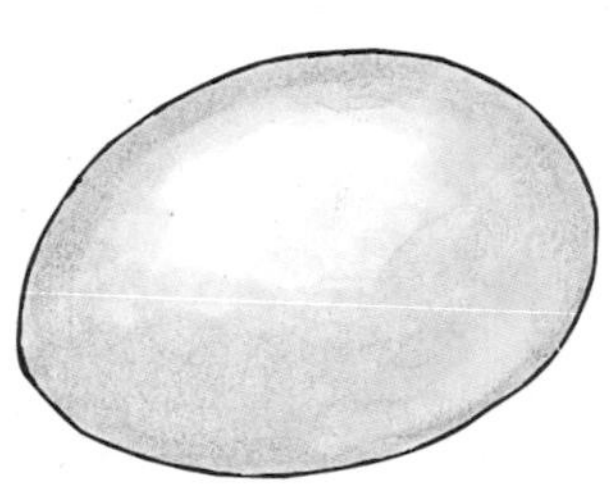

1. ____________________

I love water.

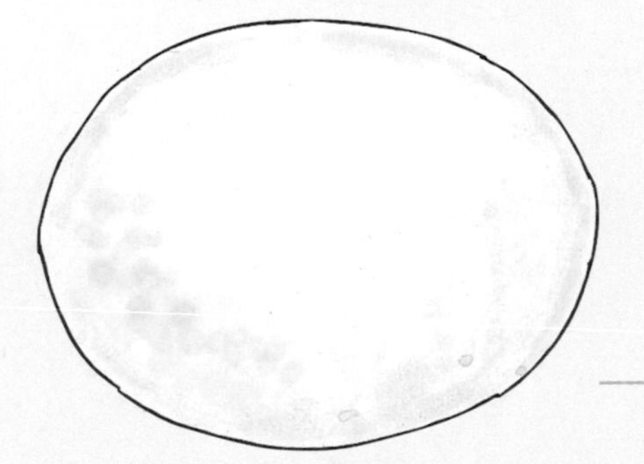

2. ____________________

I say sssss.

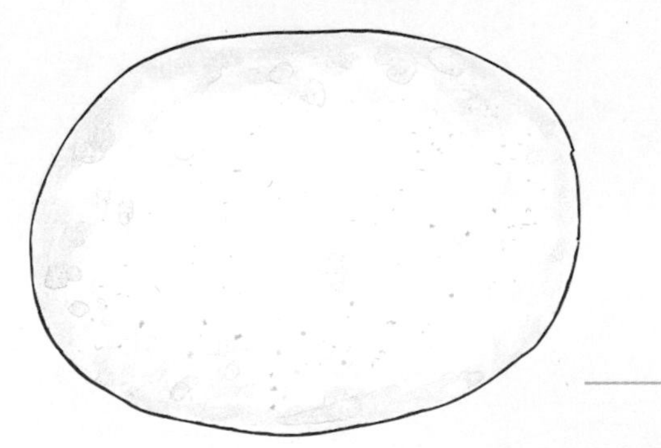

3. ____________________

I'm yellow.

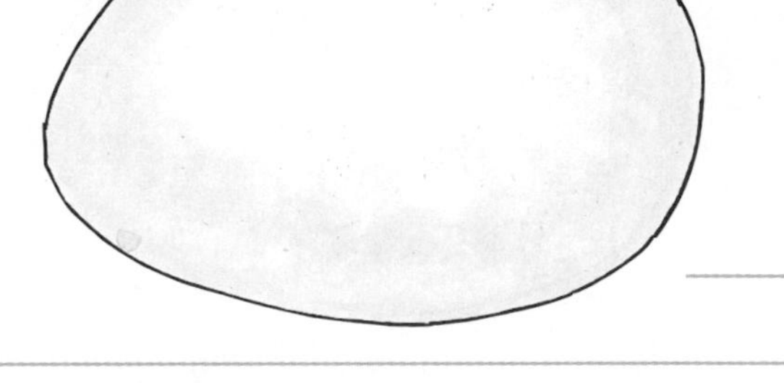

4. ____________________

Hold the page up to a light or window.
Take a peek inside each egg.
Put a ✓ by the eggs you guessed correctly.

Try This!

Fill a jar with sweets, cotton wool balls or marbles. Ask family members to guess how many are in the jar. Write down their guesses. Take a guess yourself. Then count the number. Whose guess was closest?

Let Me Out!

Were your guesses correct?
Write the animals you got wrong.

fish snake
chick robin

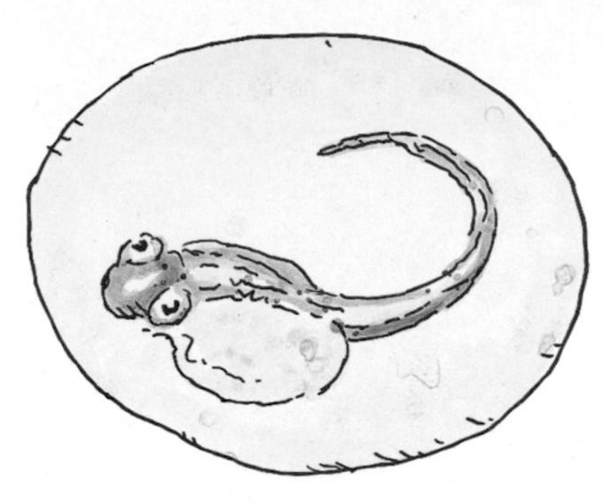

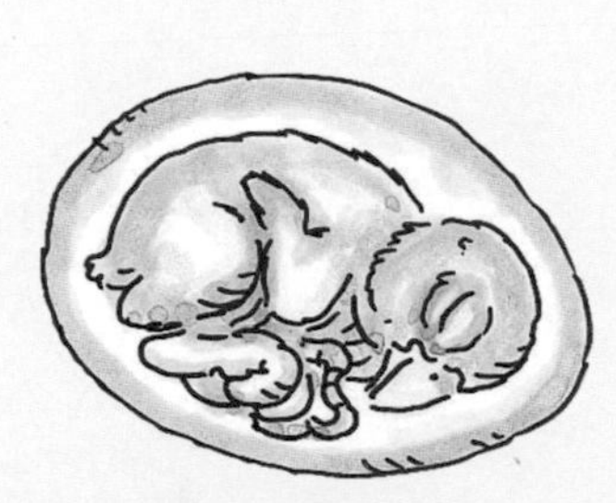

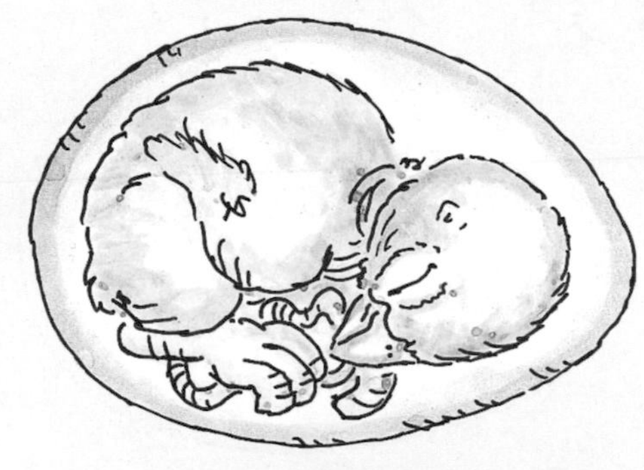

Animals use many different things to build their nests.
You can build a nest, too. You need twigs, sticks, feathers, string, grass and plastic eggs.

1. Weave small sticks and twigs together to make a bowl-shaped nest.
2. Line the nest with soft things like feathers, bits of string and grass.
3. Put the plastic eggs inside your nest.

Hiding Places

A contraction is two words put together to make one word.
A letter or letters are left out.
An apostrophe (’) takes the place of the missing letter or letters.

are not ⟶ are n t ⟶ aren’t

Circle the contraction in each sentence.
Then circle the animals in the jungle.

Draw a line from each contraction to the words that form it.

1. can’t	Where is
2. Let’s	can not
3. Where’s	is not
4. isn’t	Let us

What's Happening This Week? 

Read the zoo calendar.

Sunday	Monday	Tuesday	Wednesday	Thursday	Friday	Saturday
Sheep Shearing	Birthday Party for Coco the Camel	Storytime Safari	The Zoo Is for You Day! FREE DAY	Jungle Day Walk	Desert Trail Hike	Spring Egg Hunt 

Write the day when these things happen.

1. Tuesday

2. Wednesday

3. Munday

4. Saturday

Try This!

Make a days of the week journal. You need seven sheets of paper.

1. Write the name of a day on each page. Start with Sunday.
2. Each day, draw a picture or write about something you did.
3. Make a cover for your journal.

Sheep Shearing Today!

Write a number sentence about each picture.

1. ______ + ______ = ______

2. ______ − ______ = ______

3. ______ + ______ = ______

4. ______ − ______ = ______

5. ______ + ______ = ______

6. ______ − ______ = ______

Describe It!

Why don't baby leopards like to play hide-and-seek?

Because they are always spotted!

Describing words tell us about naming words.

The **huge** lion roared.

Which word tells us about, or **describes**, the lion?

Some describing words tell us how animals look or feel.

Write words that describe the animals.

1. ____________________ 2. ____________________

3. ____________________ 4. ____________________

5. ____________________ 6. ____________________

What a Shape!

Draw an alligator.
Follow these steps.

1. 

2. Add.

3. Add.

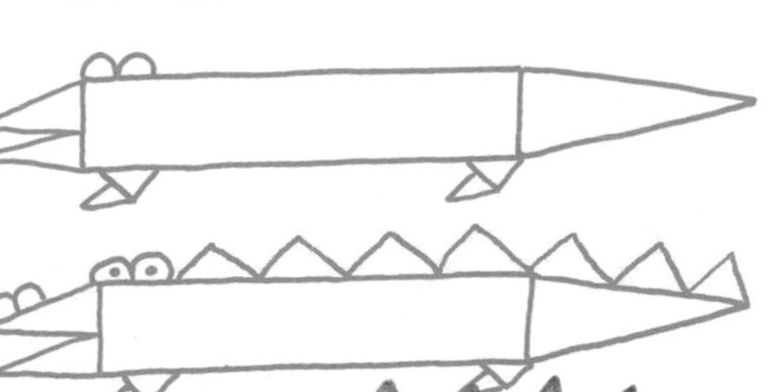

4. Add.

Draw a tiger.
Follow these steps.

1. 

2. Add.

3. Add.

4. Add.

1. How many △s in step 4?

____

2. How many ◯s in step 4?

____

Think of an animal. Make up a riddle about it. Describe how the animal looks, feels and sounds.
Example: I'm thinking of a small bird with a red head. It makes a rat-tat-tat noise. What is it? (A woodpecker)

Monkey Business

Toss a coin on the page. Read the word closest to the coin. Write the word on the chart next to the word that means the same or opposite. Play until the chart is filled.

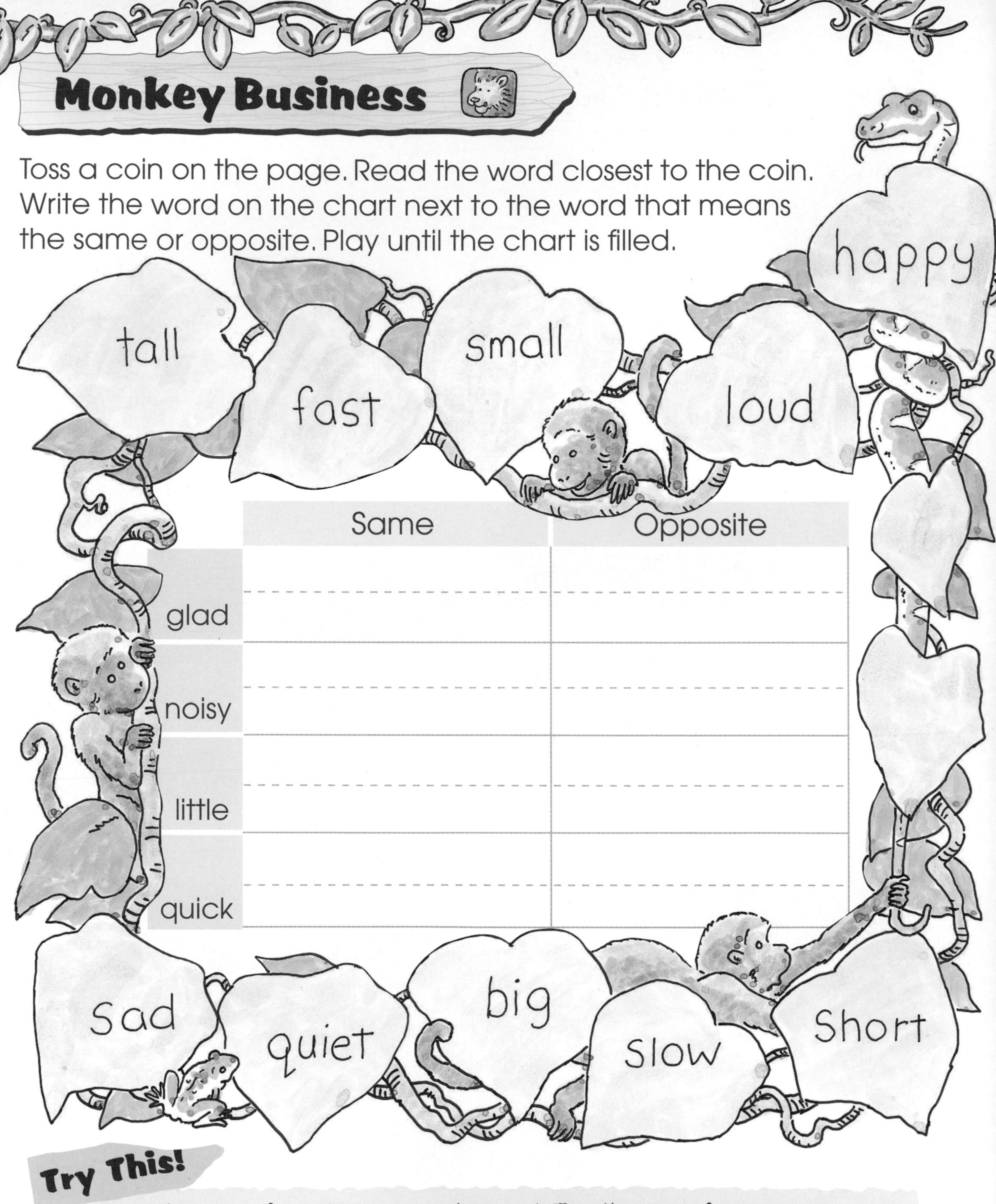

	Same	Opposite
glad		
noisy		
little		
quick		

Try This!

Copy the words from the leaves on ten cards. Turn the cards face down to play a game. Turn over two cards at a time. If the words mean the opposite, set the pair aside. If not, turn them face down again. Play until you have matched all the words.

Big Meets Little

Read the names of the big and little animals.
Add two more names to the chart.

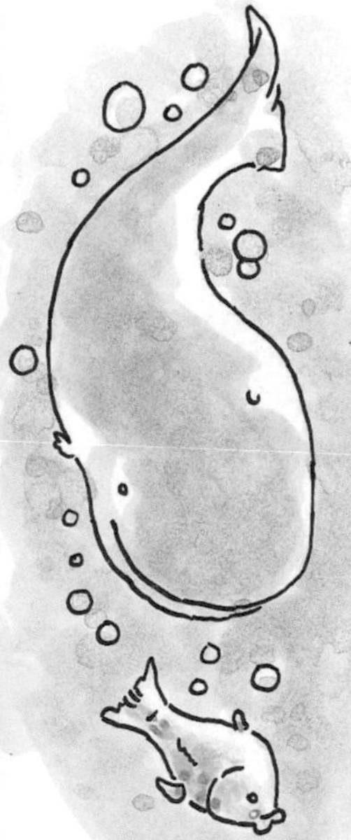

Big animals	Little animals
hippo	chipmunk
elephant	butterfly
giraffe	chick

Plan a story about two animals. Write your ideas.

Which big and little animals meet?

Where do they meet?

What is their problem?

How is the problem solved?

Little Weight Watchers  

Read the scales.

Colour in the boxes to show how many kilograms each animal weighs.

tiger cub										
baby porcupine										
fox										
snowy owl										
fawn										
opossum										
weight in kilograms	1	2	3	4	5	6	7	8	9	10

In the Seal Pool

You need 15 coins or buttons. Read the chart to find out how many to put in or take out of the pool.
Then count how many are left. Write the numerals in the chart.

Put in	Take out	How many are left?	Put in	Put in	How many in all?
9	2		9	6	
10	4		2	8	
12	7		6	5	
8	6		7	7	
15	8		8	8	

Try This!

Use the coins or buttons to write as many different maths equations that equal 15 as you can. Then write equations with three numerals that equal 15.
Example: 6 + 3 + 6 = 15

Zoomobile Tour Game   

You need a coin to toss, two buttons for markers and a sheet of paper and pencil to keep score.

1. Put your button on Start.
2. Toss the coin. If it's heads, move one space. If it's tails, move two spaces.
3. Follow the directions on the square on which you land. Make a mark on the score sheet for each right answer.
4. The game is over when you reach Finish. The most points wins.

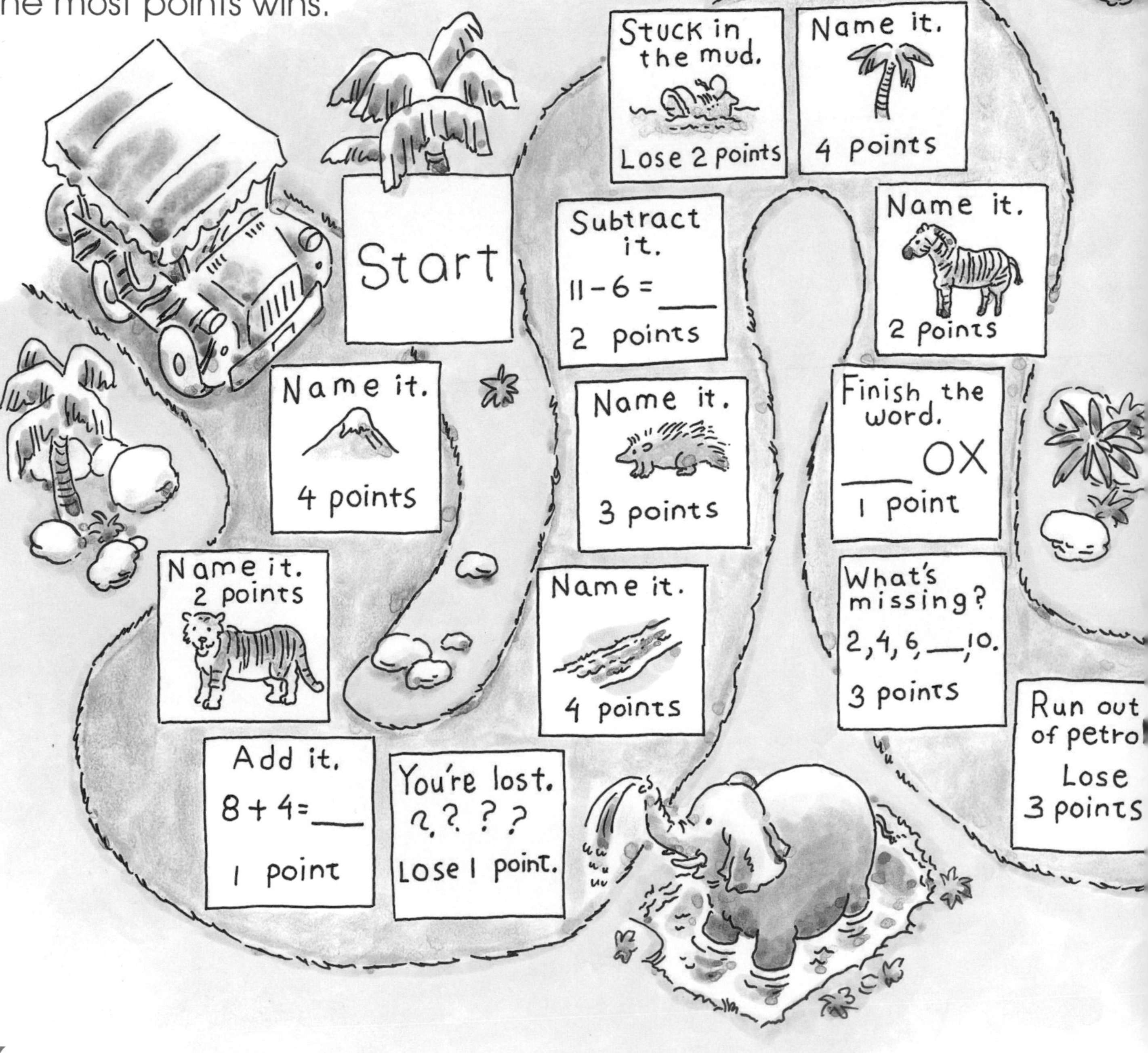

Start

Name it.
4 points

Name it.
2 points

Add it.
8 + 4 = ___
1 point

You're lost.
? ? ? ?
Lose 1 point.

Name it.
4 points

Name it.
3 points

Subtract it.
11 − 6 = ___
2 points

Stuck in the mud.
Lose 2 points

Name it.
4 points

Name it.
2 points

Finish the word.
___OX
1 point

What's missing?
2, 4, 6, ___, 10.
3 points

Run out of petro
Lose
3 points

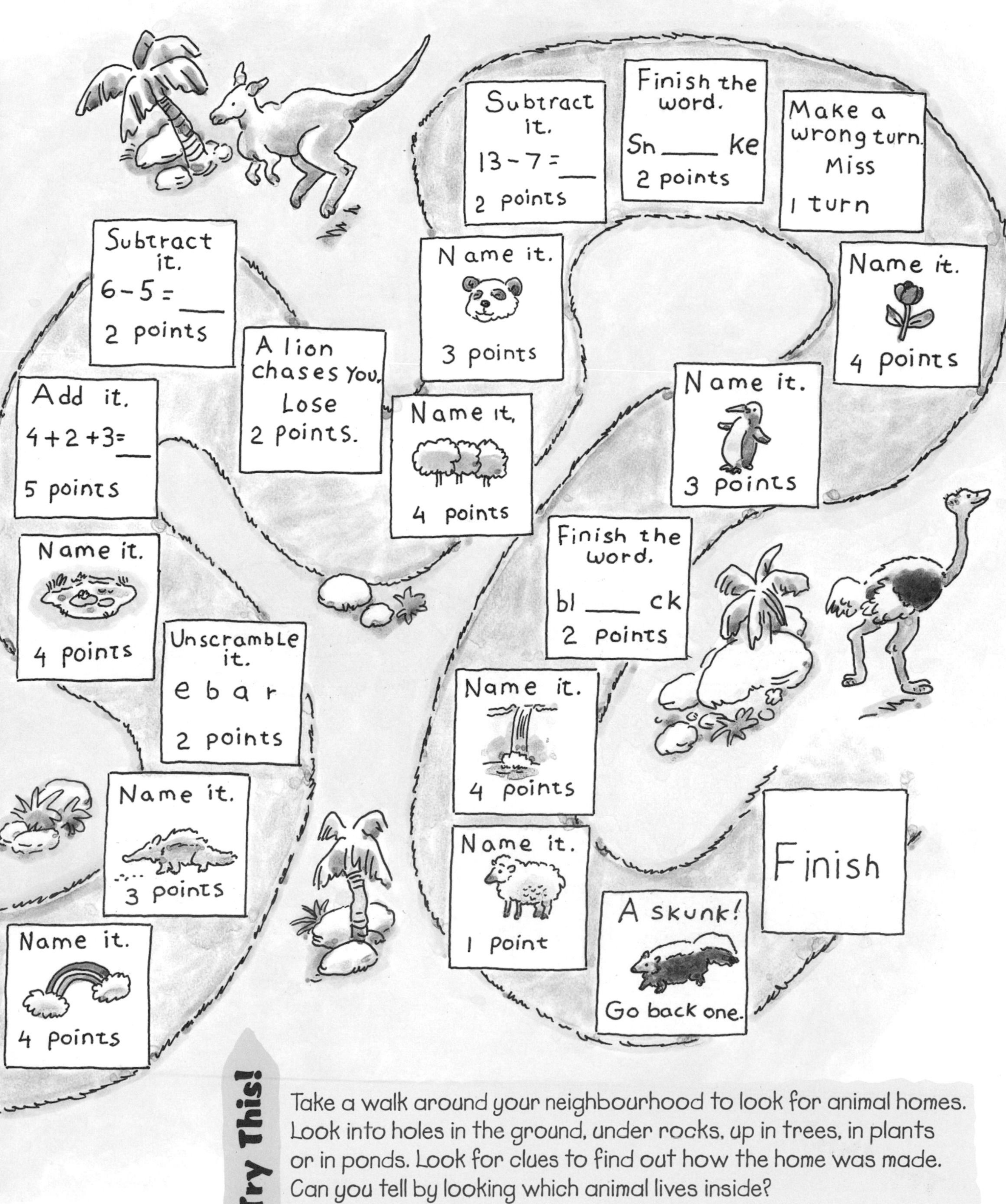

Try This!

Take a walk around your neighbourhood to look for animal homes. Look into holes in the ground, under rocks, up in trees, in plants or in ponds. Look for clues to find out how the home was made. Can you tell by looking which animal lives inside?

Critter's Cafe

Read the clues. Mark the chart with ✓s.
The first one is done for you.

1. Everyone had fruit.
2. Dad and Ben had a taco.
3. Mum had a salad.
4. Anna had a turkey sandwich.
5. Mum, Ben and Anna had juice.
6. Dad had milk.

	milk	juice	fruit	salad	taco	sandwich
Dad			✓			
Ben			✓			
Mum			✓			
Anna			✓			

Write a person's name under each meal.

1. ______________________

2. ______________________

3. ______________________

4. ______________________

Make critter place-mats. You need card, crayons or pens, and clear laminate. Draw animals on the card. Cover with clear laminate.

Guess Who's Coming to Dinner

Start at 2. Connect the dots counting by twos from 2 to 40.

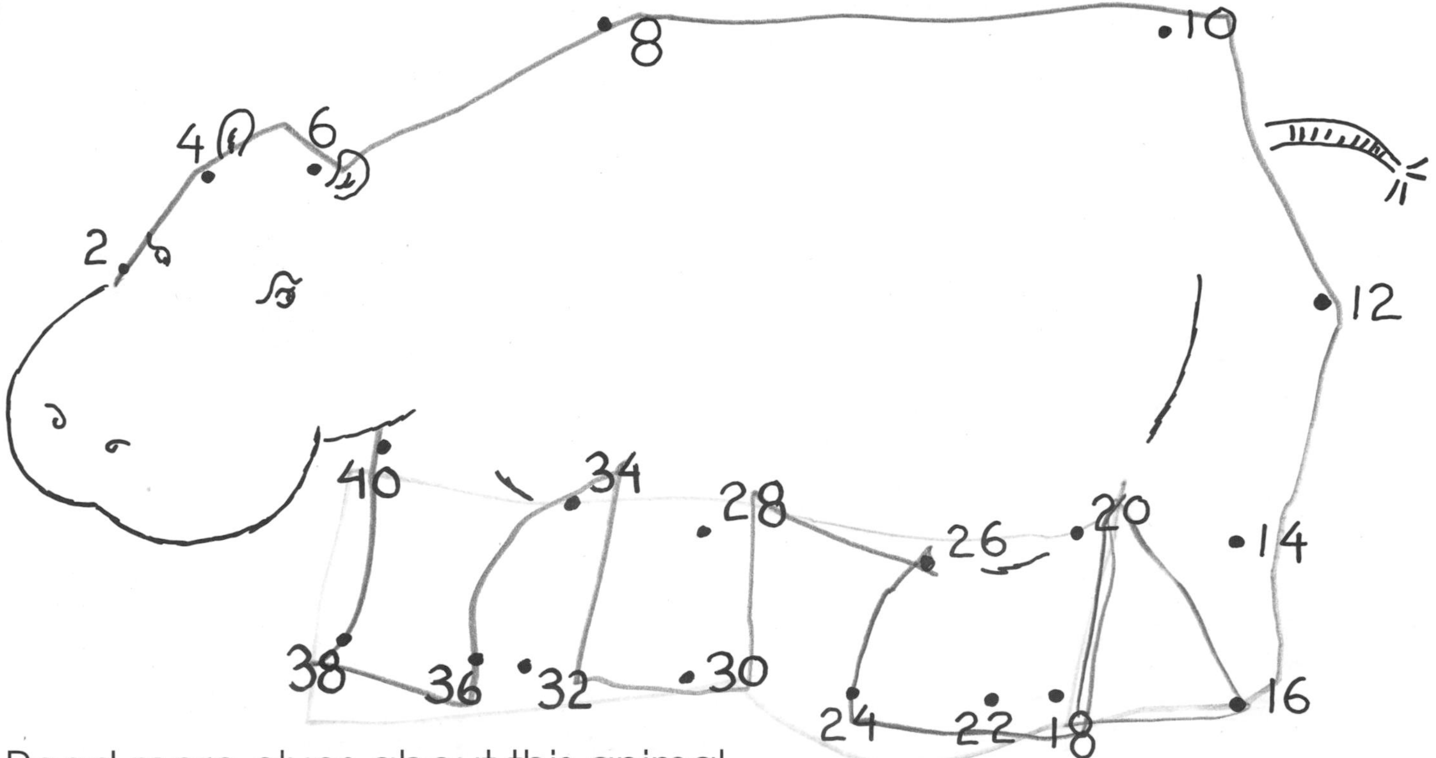

Read more clues about this animal.
Write the words from the circle in the sentences.

hippo
grass
fat
water

1. This animal is very ______________________ .

2. It spends the day in ______________________ and eats at night.

3. It can eat 40 kilograms of ______________________ each night.

4. This animal is a ______________________ .

Who Is Lost?

Dad went to buy popcorn. Now he is lost.
Circle the right answers to help him find the family.

1. Where should Dad walk first?

    to the office   to the water fountain   to the zoo entrance

2. Next, Dad should walk to the ___.

    flag   rubbish bin   pond

3. Dad will see the family on the bench if he walks by the ___.

    office   pond   parrot

4. Write **1**, **2**, **3** to show the right order.

    ________ flag   ________ fountain   ________ parrot

5. Draw a red line on the path Dad should take.

Ape Escape

Help the ape get to the banana tree.
Count in fives from **5** to **50**.
Colour the squares with these numbers to show the path.

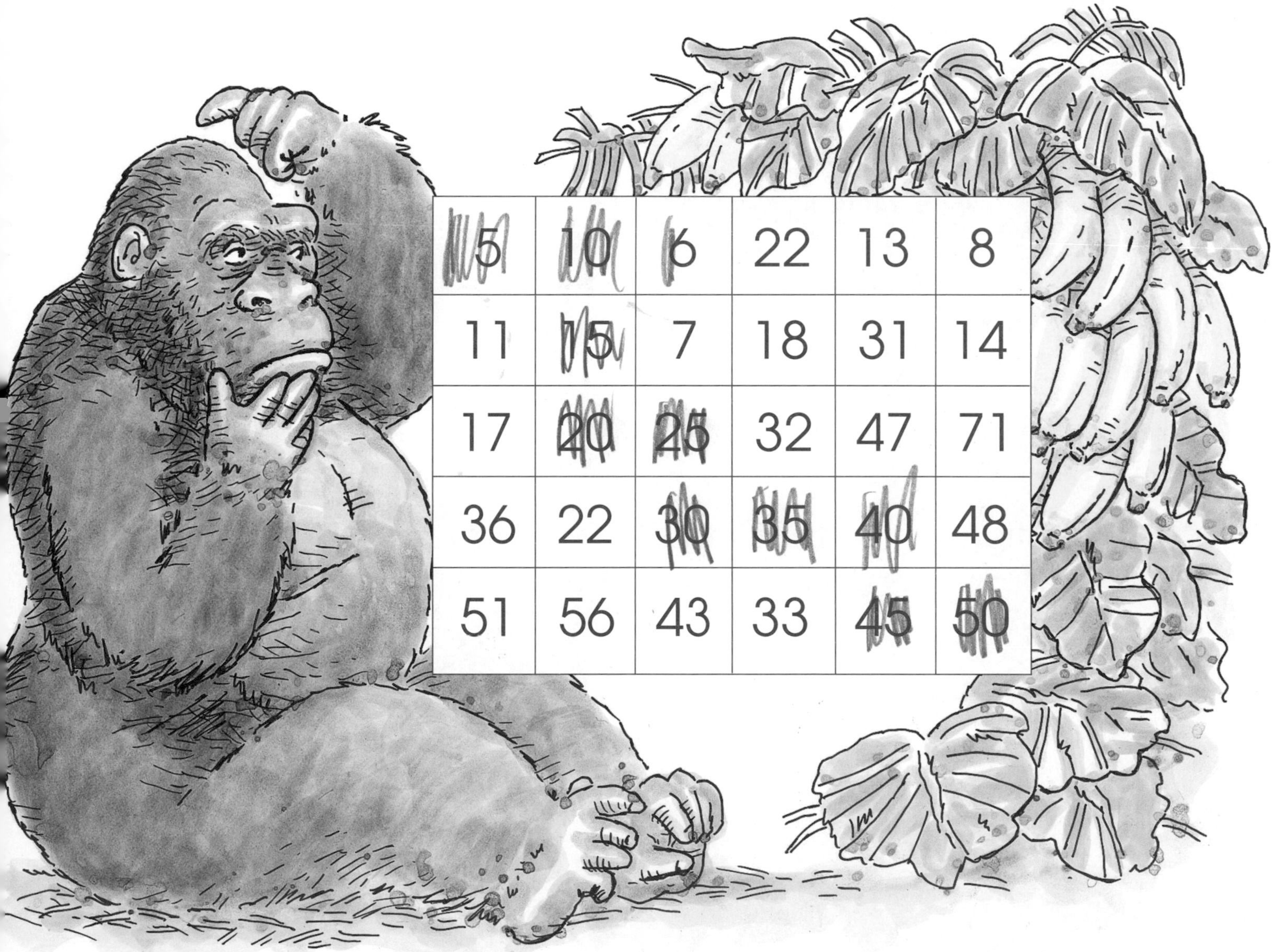

5	10	6	22	13	8
11	15	7	18	31	14
17	20	25	32	47	71
36	22	30	35	40	48
51	56	43	33	45	50

Try This!

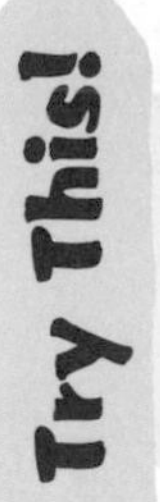

Try counting backwards from 50 to 5. Then count in twos from 30 to 2. Count in tens from 100 to 10. How fast can you count?

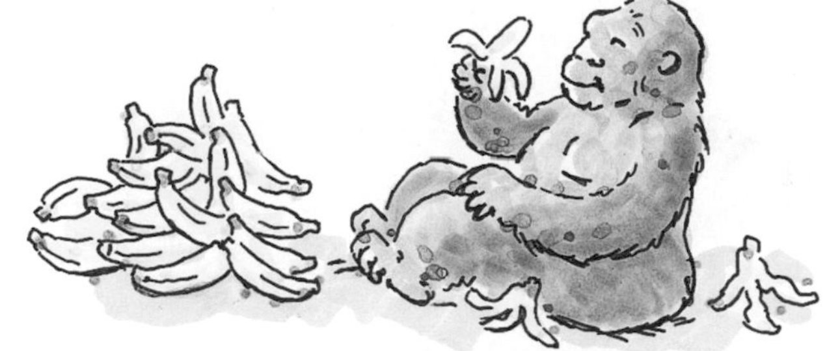

Yipes Stripes!

Look at each row.
Draw the missing picture to fit the pattern.

1.

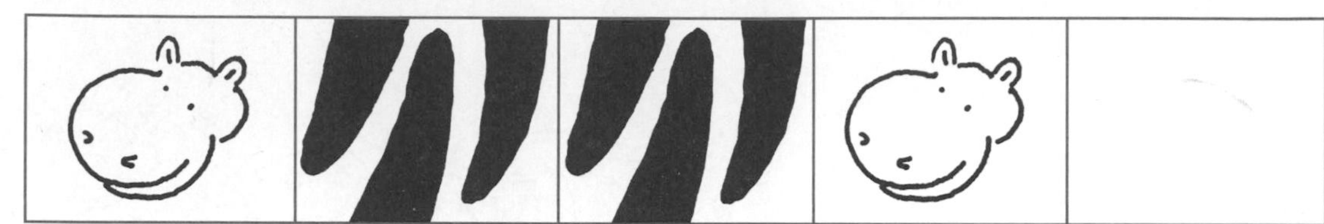

2.

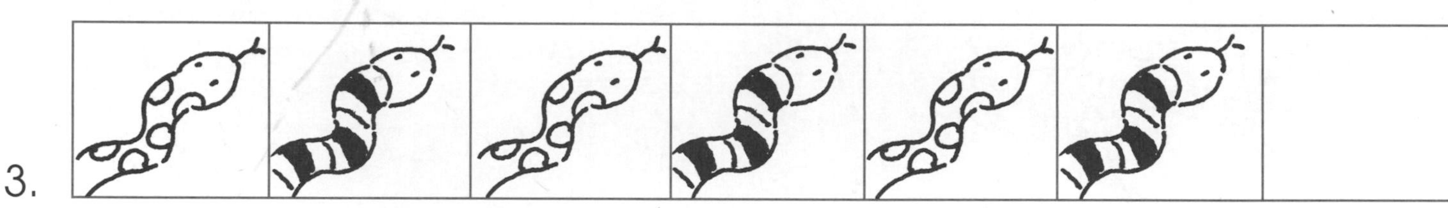

3.

4. Help the tiger get to her cubs. Find the pattern.
Colour the shapes to finish the path.

Try This!

Collect leaves and flower petals. Glue them on paper to form different patterns.

Get Out of Here!

Look at each group of animals.
Circle the one that does not belong.
Then draw an animal that belongs.

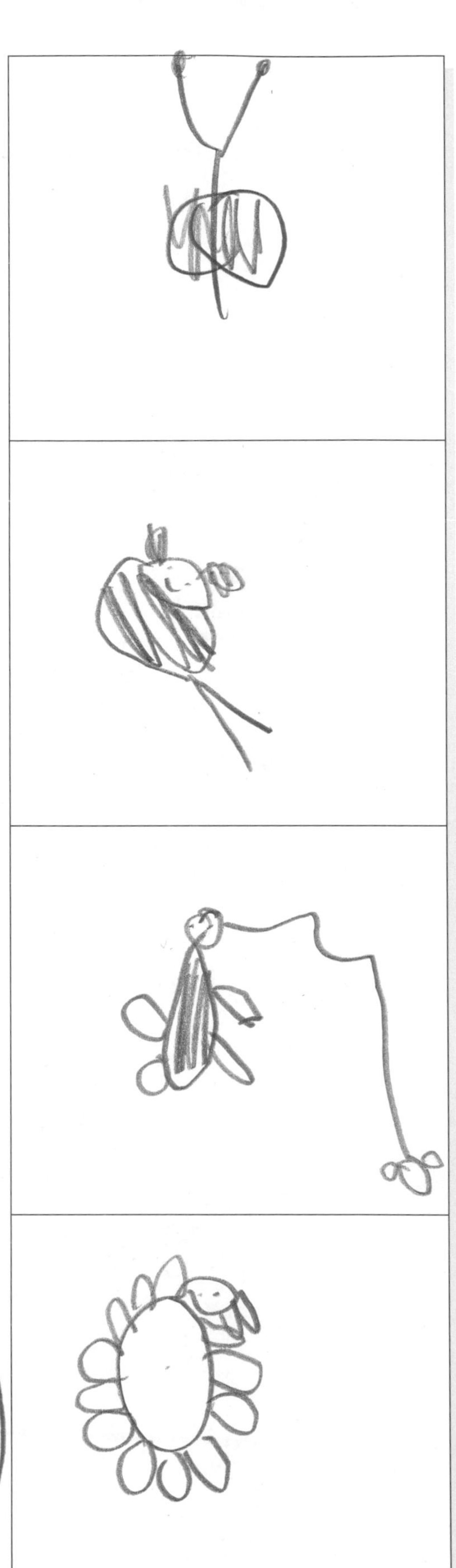

Forest Theatre 

A sentence ends with a full stop. (.)
A question ends with a question mark. (?)

Read the sign. Add a (.) or a (?) in the ◯ at the end of each sentence.

Forest Theatre

1. The theatre is open from 9:00 to 5:00 ◯
2. Have you ever seen an opossum ◯
3. Do you know what a deer eats ◯
4. Come see the show to find out ◯
5. You will meet many forest friends ◯

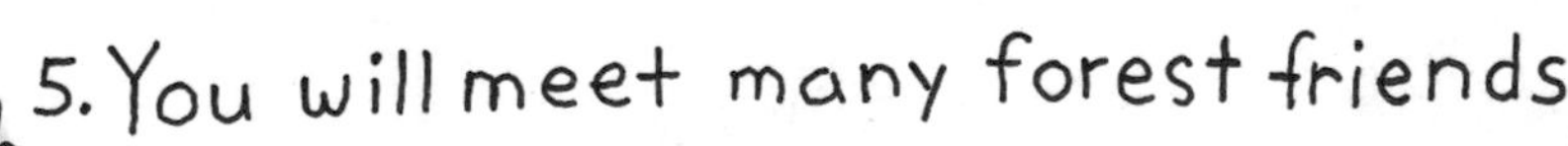

The Big Screen  

Write the letters under the numbers.
The first letter is done for you. Then read each animal name.
Draw a line to match the name to the picture.

1	2	3	4	5	6	7	8	9	10	11	12	13	14	15	16
a	b	c	d	e	i	k	l	m	n	o	p	q	r	s	u

The Stars of the Show

1.

11	12	11	15	15	16	9
o						

2.

4	5	5	14

3.

15	7	16	10	7

4.

15	13	16	6	14	14	5	8

Try This!

Finish this riddle about one of the stars of the show. Write your own words. Ask someone to guess your riddle.

This animal lives in the forest.
Its colour is ______________.
It has ______________.
What is it? ______________.

Rise and Shine! 

When does each animal get up in the morning?
Write the time.

Try This!

Ask someone to use a clock with a second hand to time you. Guess how many numbers you can write in one minute. Then do it. How close was your guess?

What do you say to a clock at noon?

Hands up!

Froggy Grows Up

Look at the pictures.

A B C D E

Read the sentences.
Write **A**, **B**, **C**, **D** and **E** to show how Froggy grows up.

1. ________ Froggy is a tiny tadpole.
2. ________ Froggy is a big frog.
3. ________ Froggy is an egg.
4. ________ Froggy grows four legs.
5. ________ Froggy grows two legs.

Animal Poll

The zookeeper is counting the animals with hooves.
She needs more animals for the zoo.
Fill in the chart to show how many more she needs.

Kinds of animals	Animals we want	Animals we have	How many more do we need?
camel	8	4	
deer	15	9	
giraffe	10	7	
hippo	12	8	
pig	14	7	
sheep	18	9	
buffalo	9	5	
moose	13	6	

Have you ever seen a coin with a picture of an animal on it?
You can design your own coin.

1. Cut a large circle from paper or use a white paper plate.
2. Choose an animal for your coin.
3. Draw what your coin will look like.

Who Is Hiding?

One animal with hooves is very shy.
He is hiding behind these numbers.
Find the sums and differences of the numbers in each row.
Then use the code to find out the animal's name.

7	8	9	10	11	12	13	14	15
r	e	s	m	t	o	f	s	v

5	12	8	5	10
+8	-6	+2	+7	-3
-7	+3	-5	-6	+7
+4	+3	+7	+8	-6

Look at the last number in each row. Write the letter from the code box to spell the animal's name.

A Tale of Tracks 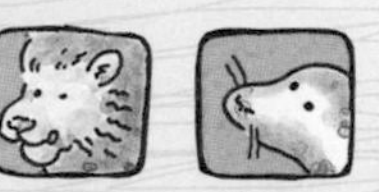

Read the story.

Last night we saw some **tracks**. The tracks came from the **forest** . They went by the tree . Then they went down to the pond . We followed the tracks to our house . What is all that noise? A hungry visitor is eating dinner!

Look at the garden. Follow the tracks.
Number the places from 1 to 4.

Be a Detective

Look at the story on page 46.
Answer the questions.

1. A fox has four toes on each paw.
   Is the visitor a fox? Yes No
2. A deer has hooves.
   Is it a deer? Yes No
3. A squirrel has four toes on its front paws and five toes on its hind paws.
   Is it a squirrel? Yes No
4. **What** did you see?

5. **Where** did they come from?

6. **When** did this happen?

Try This!

Look for tracks in your garden.

1. Go outside. Spread some sand on the ground.
2. Place bird seed, nuts, bread and fruit slices in the centre.
3. Stay away for a day. Then check for animal tracks.
4. What do you see? Three toes might mean a bird was there.
   Four toes might mean a fox.

Spending Money

Count the money. Write the amounts on the lines.
Is there enough money to buy the item?
Circle **Yes** or **No**. The first one is done for you.

Try This!

Play Jumble Sale with some friends. Use self-stick notes to label prices on things around the house. Buy and sell the things you labelled using coins or play money.

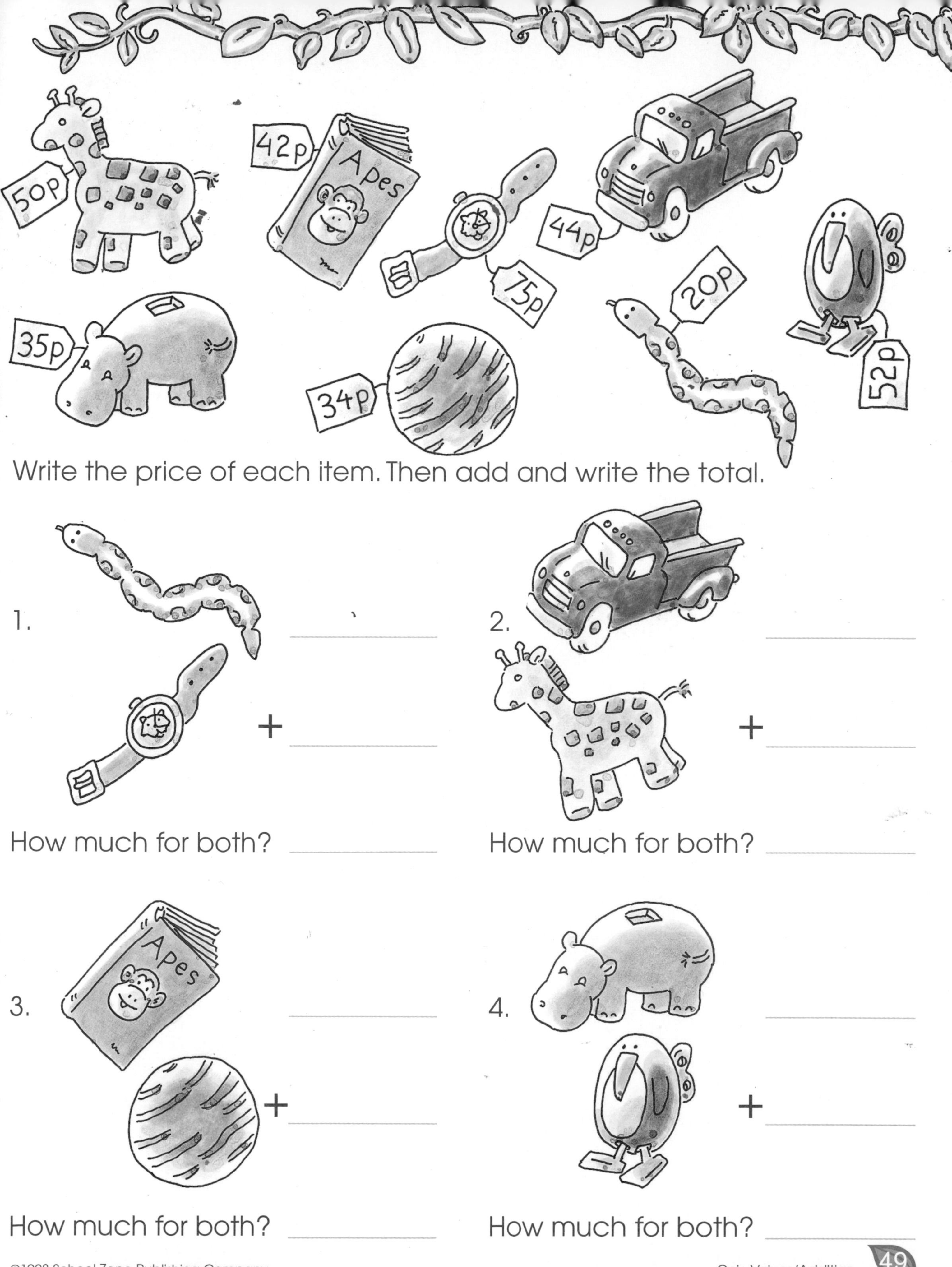

Write the price of each item. Then add and write the total.

1. ______

\+ ______

How much for both? ______

2. ______

\+ ______

How much for both? ______

3. ______

\+ ______

How much for both? ______

4. ______

\+ ______

How much for both? ______

Parts of a Whole 

A fraction is a part of a whole.

$\frac{1}{4}$ → part shaded / parts in all

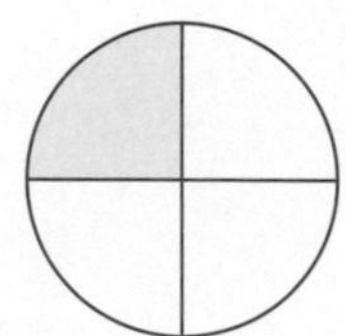

Colour the shapes to show the fractions.

$\frac{1}{2}$

$\frac{1}{4}$

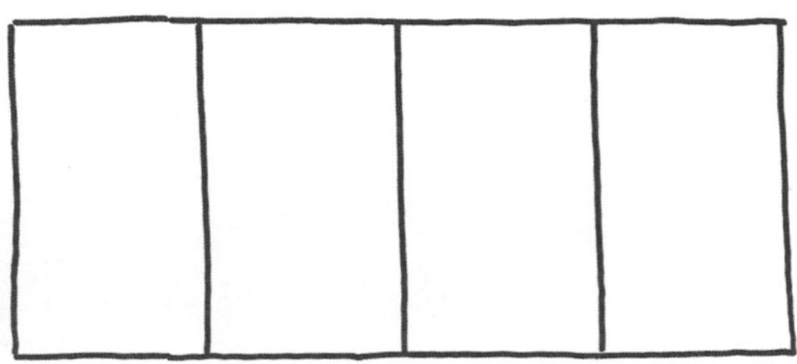

$\frac{1}{3}$

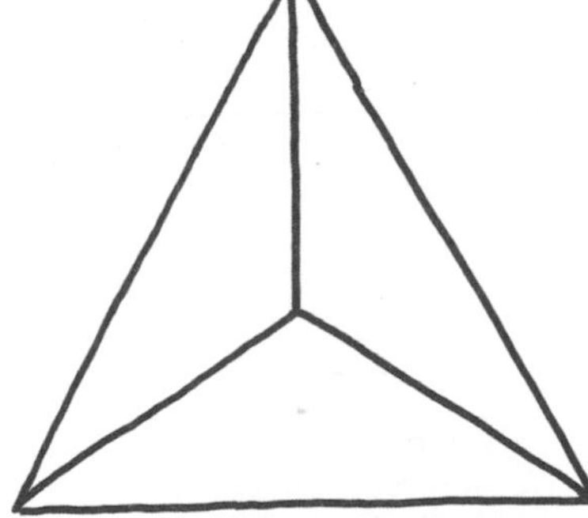

$\frac{2}{2}$

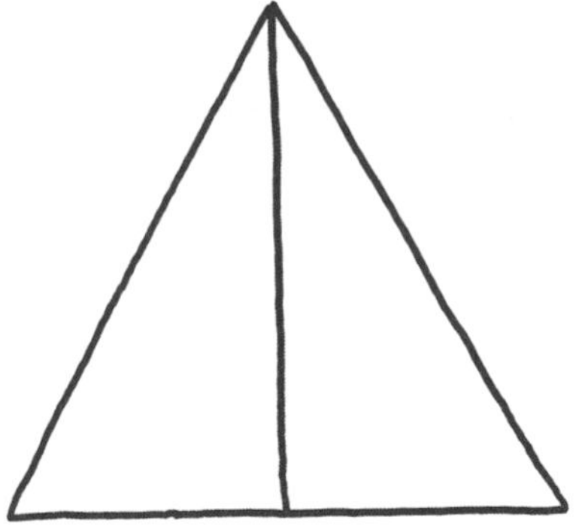

$\frac{3}{4}$

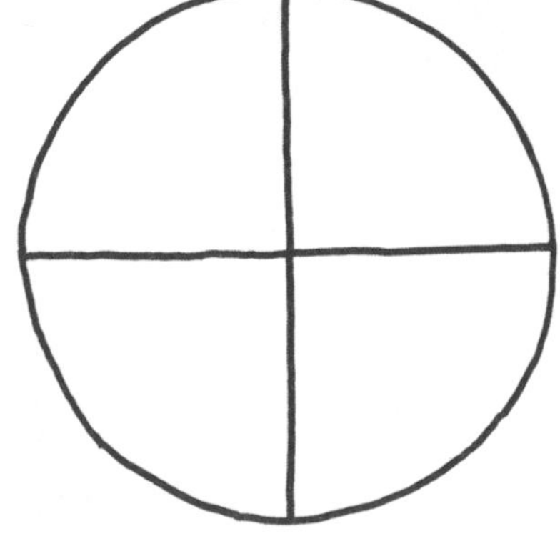

$\frac{2}{3}$

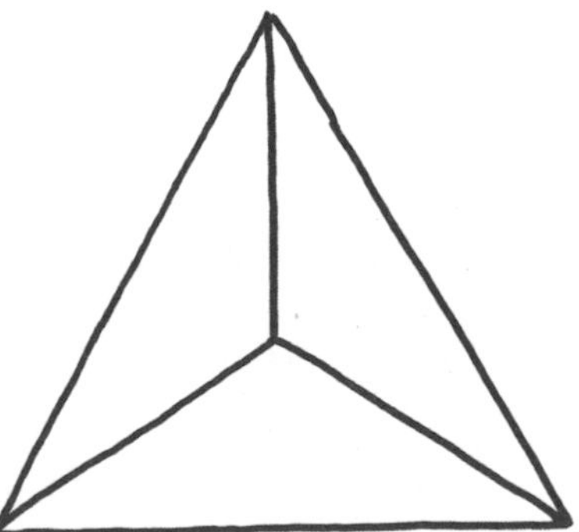

What do zoo animals eat? Draw a line from each word to the food.
Colour foods in each group to show the fraction.

apples **carrots** **bananas** **oranges** **hay** **lettuce**

1. $\frac{2}{4}$

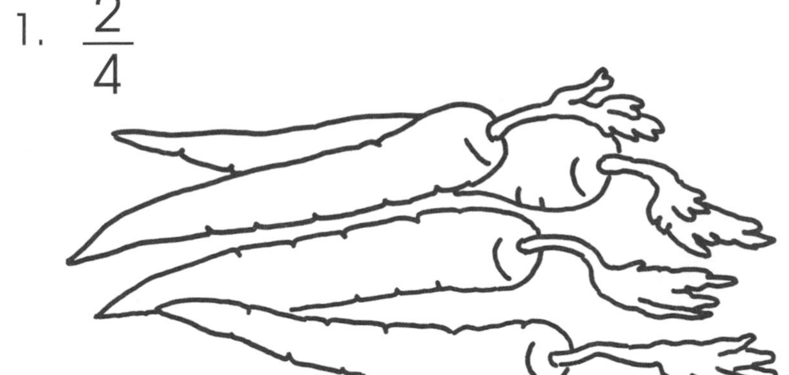

2. $\frac{2}{5}$

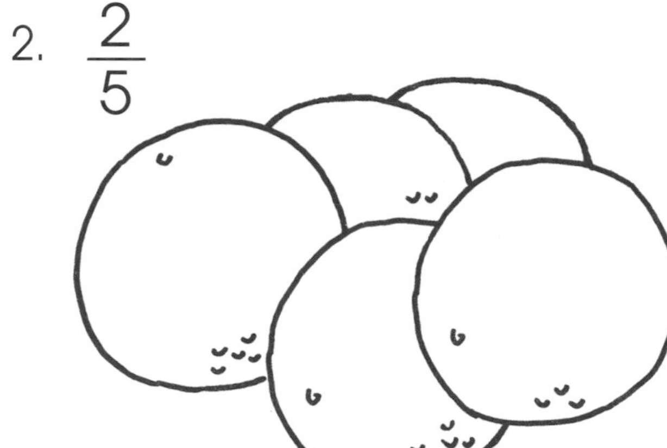

3. $\frac{1}{3}$

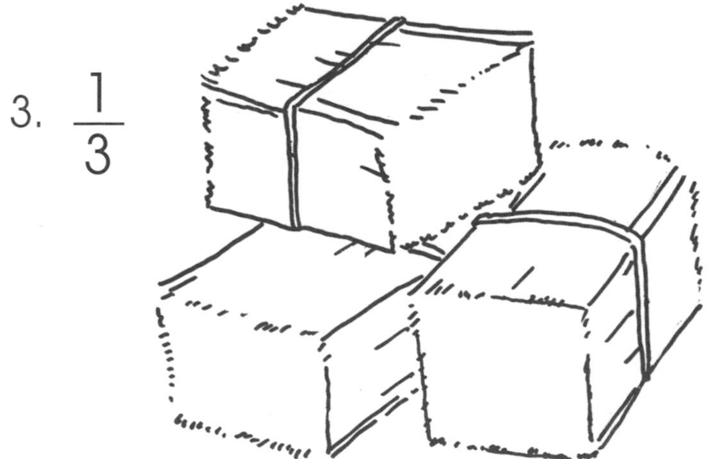

4. $\frac{1}{4}$

5. $\frac{2}{3}$

6. $\frac{1}{2}$

Butterfly Garden 

Take the family through the butterfly garden. Answer each problem in the space that follows it. Then circle the hidden butterflies.

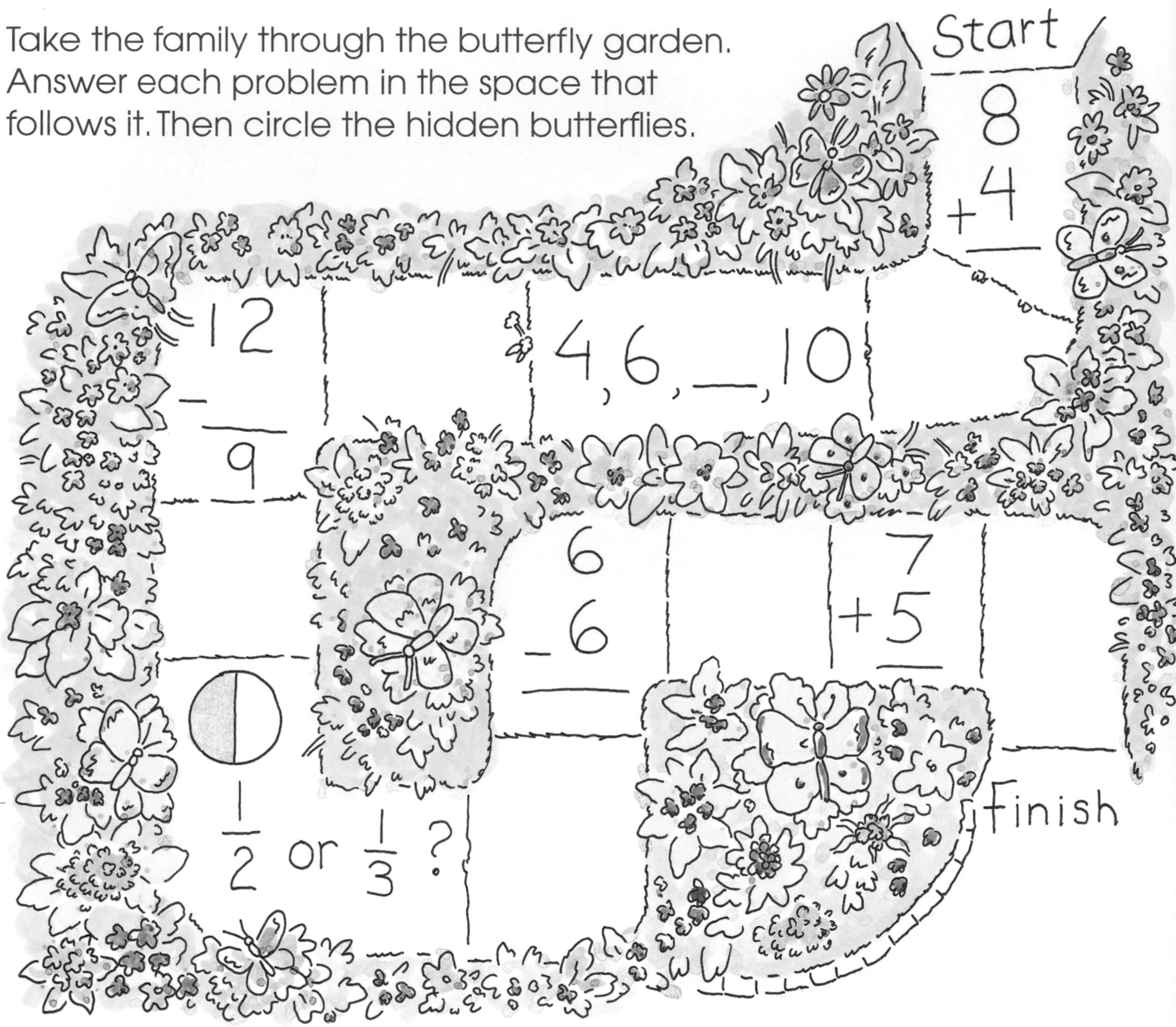

Start

$8 + 4 = $ ___

$12 - $ ___ $= 9$

4, 6, ___, 10

$6 - 6 = $ ___

$7 + 5 = $ ___

$\frac{1}{2}$ or $\frac{1}{3}$?

Finish

How many butterflies did you find? ___________

Try This!

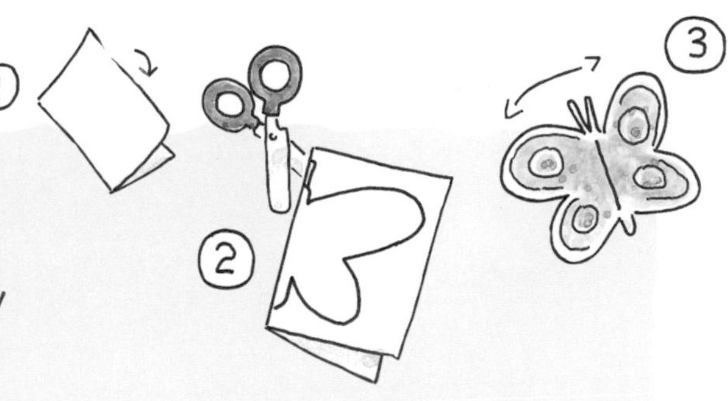

The right half of a butterfly is the same as the left half. You need paper, scissors and crayons. Fold a sheet of paper in half. Draw half of a butterfly. Cut out the shape. Then unfold it. Colour both halves the same way.

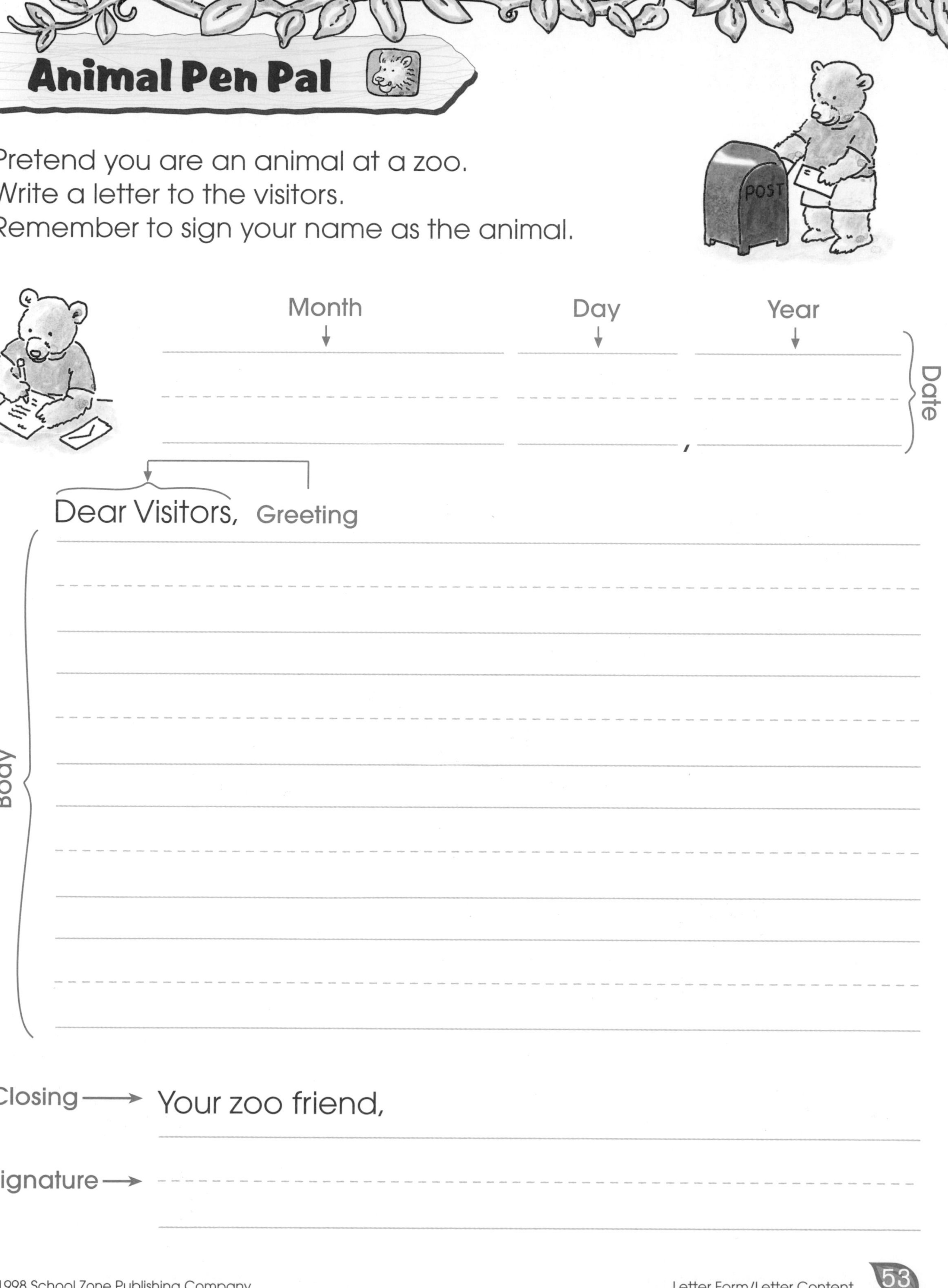

Animal Pen Pal

Pretend you are an animal at a zoo.
Write a letter to the visitors.
Remember to sign your name as the animal.

A Tale of a Tail

A bear's tail is short and stubby.
One Native American tale explains why.

Once, bears  had **long, furry tails**. Then something happened. Bear  was hungry for crayfish. But the pond 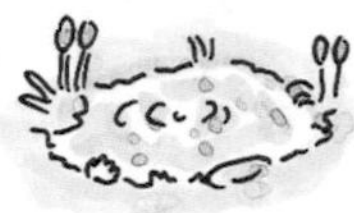 was frozen. So Bear  asked Fox  for help. Tricky Fox  told Bear to make a hole in the ice. He told Bear  to hang his long tail through the hole. When a crayfish  pinched it, he could pull the crayfish  up. Bear  felt a pinch. But it it was not a crayfish . His tail was frozen into the pond . Bear  pulled so hard that his tail broke off. Bears  have had **short tails** ever since.

Try This!

Write your own tale. Think of an animal and what is special about it. Describe how it got to be that way. Draw pictures to go with your story.

1. What kind of tail did bears once have?

2. What kind of tails do bears have now?

3. Why did bears' tails change?

Compare the Bears!

Black Bears:1.2–1.5 metres long; 68–182 kilograms
Grizzly Bears: 1.8–2.2 metres long; 136-408 kilograms
Polar Bears: 1.8–2.4 metres long, up to 680 kilograms
Coastal Brown Bears: 1.8–2.6 metres long; up to 726 kilograms

Animal Count

In this picture are some of the animals you met in this book.
Guess how many there are. ☐

Now count the animals.
Watch out!
Some animals are hiding.
How close was your guess? ☐

Be a Poet

There are many reasons people like zoos.
Write some of your reasons here to finish this poem.

Zoos

I like zoos.
I'll tell you why.
Because,

Because,

Because,

Because! That's why!
I like zoos.

Try This!

Make an animal puppet to help you say your poem. You need a paper bag, card, scissors, glue, crayons and felt-tip pens. Draw a face on the flap at the bottom of the bag.

1. Cut out and add ears.
2. Add a mouth and feet, paws or wings.
3. Put your hand inside the bag. Move the flap up and down to make your puppet talk.

Activities to Share: English

Here is a list of excellent animal books to look for in your local library or bookstore. The list includes fiction and nonfiction.

- *Crocodile Smile* by Sarah Weeks, illustrated by Lois Ehlert. HarperCollins, 1994. Bright picture collages enhance this book of animal songs and poems. The book comes with a cassette tape.

- *From Head to Toe* by Eric Carle. HarperCollins, 1997. A variety of familiar animals invites the reader to copy their antics as they wiggle, stomp, thump and bend across the pages of this book.

- *The Great Kapok Tree: A Tale of the Amazon Rain Forest* by Lynne Cherry. Gulliver Books, Harcourt, 1990. The great kapok tree is in danger of being cut down. What will happen to all the forest creatures if this occurs?

- *A Hippopotamusn't and Other Animal Poems* by J. Patrick Lewis. Dial Books, 1990. This is a collection of funny verse about all kinds of animals. The humorous illustrations add to the fun.

- *How the Guinea Fowl Got Her Spots: An African Tale* retold and illustrated by Barbara Knutson. Carolrhoda, 1990. When Guinea Fowl helps her friend escape from a lion, she is rewarded with a disguise that will camouflage her.

- *In the Small, Small Pond* by Denise Fleming. Henry Holt, 1993. Spring has sprung, and a bright green frog leaps out of the grass and into the pond where a host of other animals make their homes. The reader follows tadpoles, minnows, turtles, dragonflies and ducks through spring, summer and autumn. When winter arrives, the frog burrows deep into the pond to wait for spring's return.

- *Penguin Pete and Little Tim* by Marcus Pfister. North-South Books, 1994. Penguin Pete is a proud father who cannot wait to show his son the wonders of their chilly world.

- *Time to Sleep* by Denise Fleming. Henry Holt, 1997. The chill in the air tells Bear that it's time for her winter-long nap. She must tell Snail, who tells Skunk, who tells Turtle. Each puts off going to sleep in order to see, smell, hear and taste the signs of the season.

- *V for Vanishing: An Alphabet of Endangered Animals* by Patricia Mullins. HarperCollins, 1994. Beautiful collages depict many animals that are in danger of extinction.

There are many things your family can do to help preserve the environment and help save endangered animals. Here are some suggestions.

In Your Home

Recycle everything you can: newspapers, glass, cans, aluminium, motor oil, scrap metal.
Save kitchen scraps for a compost heap.
Use phosphate-free dish and washing powder.
Avoid using pesticides.
Use cold water in the sink whenever possible.
Use cloth napkins and washable rags.
Reuse brown paper and plastic bags.
Use plastic storage food containers rather than foil or plastic wrap.
Turn down the heat one degree for each hour you are away from home or asleep.
Turn off lights and the television when you are not in the room.
Feed the birds; make birdhouses and bird baths.
Compost leaves and garden debris.

When Shopping

Don't buy foods in styrofoam or plastic containers if there is an alternative.
Avoid disposable items. If you must buy disposables, buy paper rather than plastics.
Put parcels in one large sack rather than many small bags.
Buy in bulk and buy locally grown products.

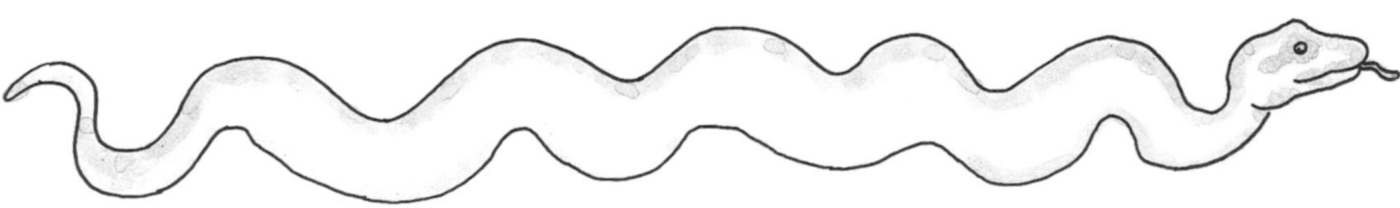

Science

- Some experts claim that there has been a 50% reduction in the population of songbirds over the past century. Do some simple projects with your child to house and feed some feathered friends. The world's easiest birdhouse to make uses a 15 to 20 cm green and orange gourd. Drill or whittle an opening for the bird. Scrape out the seeds. Drill or whittle a 1 cm drain hole at the bottom and a 0.5 cm hole through the top to insert a line for hanging. This house will last for one season.

- To feed the birds, sew a garland of popcorn, grain cereals and dried fruits to hang in the trees. Or smear peanut butter on pine cones and sprinkle with seeds.

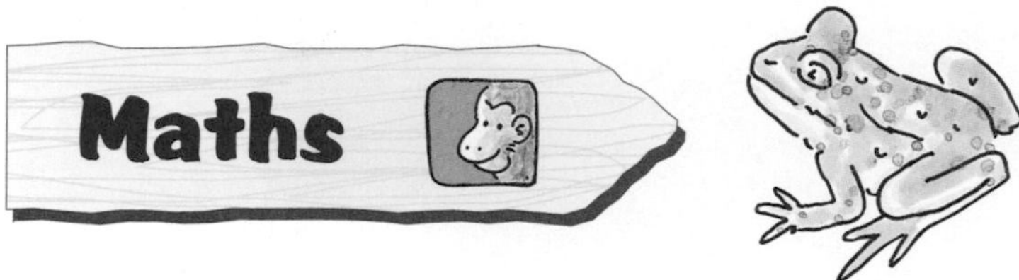

Maths

Take maths into the kitchen where you and your child can make animal-theme foods for a snack or meal. Here are two suggestions.

- Hippo-Hip Hooray Salad
  For each salad: 1 lettuce leaf, 1 pear half, cheese triangles, 2 raisins, 2 cherries

  1. Place a lettuce leaf on a plate.
  2. Top with a pear half, placing the sliced side down.
  3. Add cheese triangle ears, raisin eyes and cherry nose.
     Make one salad for each family member.

- A Hoot of a Treat
  For each treat: 1 slice of wheat bread, tuna or chicken salad, 2 slices of egg and black olives, 1 triangle of cheese, pine nuts

  1. Cut the bread on one end to form owl's head.
  2. Cover the bread with a favourite spread.
  3. Place 2 egg slices with black olive slices for eyes.
  4. Add a cheese beak and pine nuts for claws. Enjoy!

Answers

Pages 2–3

Bank, Fire Station, Grocers, Hospital, Post Office, School, Toy Shop, Zippity Zoo

Page 7

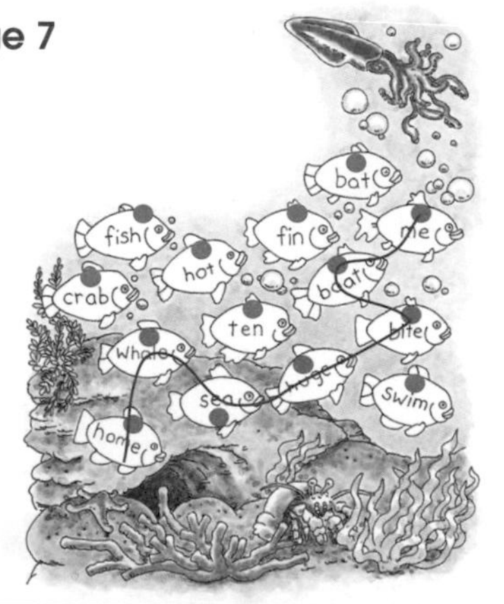

Page 11

1. snake 2. swan
3. spider 4. skunk
5. slug 6. starfish

x	b	s	k	u	n	k
v	s	t	o	p	s	g
s	w	a	n	g	n	s
f	t	r	y	c	o	l
t	u	f	z	j	w	u
s	p	i	d	e	r	g
y	o	s	n	a	k	e
p	q	h	s	n	a	p

Page 14

Circle Jan, Bob, Chan and Lisa.
1. Bob 2. Jan 3. Lisa 4. Chan

Pages 4–5

4. Answers will vary.
5. yes
6. yes
7. no

Page 8

fast, stop, top, pat, ten, tent, tub, bat at, trap, rap, pot; *counterclockwise*: fat, top, par, part, tab, but, net, tap, pot, pots

Page 12

missing numerals: 4, 3, 6, 5, 6, 9, 6, 10, 8, 11, 6

Page 15

1. Jungle World
2. Quackers Pond
3. Zebra Park
4. Monkey Island
Bear Cave

Page 19

1. slide
2. jump
3. dig
4. climb

Page 6

1. swan 2. bobcat 3. zebra

Page 9

number words: five, one, four, four, one, three, three, one, two, two, one, one, one
words that rhyme with tip: 1. dip 2. slip 3. trip 4. flip; other words: chip, clip, drip, hip, grip, lip, nip, rip, ship, sip, skip, snip, yip, zip

Page 10

1. 3 2. 6
3. 3 or 8 4. 2
5. 4 6. 1

Page 13

1. under 2. on 3. over
4. across 5. in

page 16

4 + 3 = 7 tigers
6 + 3 = 9 leopards
4 + 2 = 6 bobcats
5 + 4 = 9 lions

Pages 17–18

1. Names will vary. 2. 1 + 2 = 3
3. 3 - 1 = 2 4. 2 + 3 = 5
5. 5 - 2 = 3 6. 3 + 3 = 6
7. 6 - 2 = 4 8. 4 - 4 = 0

Page 20

1. pup 2. cub

Pages 21–22

1. robin
2. fish
3. snake
4. chick

Page 23

1. can't — can not
2. Let's — Let us
3. Where's — Where is
4. isn't — is not

Page 24

1. Tuesday 2. Thursday
3. Monday 4. Saturday

Page 25

1. 6 + 4 = 10 2. 5 - 4 = 1
3. 4 + 2 = 6 4. 5 - 3 = 2
5. 7 + 5 = 12 6. 5 - 2 = 3

Page 26

1. wet 2. huge
3. tiny 4. sleepy
5. long 6. tall

Page 27

1. 14
2. 2

Page 28

glad: happy, sad
noisy: loud, quiet
little: small, big
quick: fast, slow

Page 29

Animal names will vary.
Stories will vary. Make sure that stories have two characters that solve a problem.

Page 30

tiger cub										
baby porcupine										
fox										
snowy owl										
fawn										
opossum										
weight in kilograms	1	2	3	4	5	6	7	8	9	10

Page 31

Put in	Take out	How many are left?	Put in	Put in	How many in all?
9	2	7	9	6	15
10	4	6	2	8	10
12	7	5	6	5	11
8	6	2	7	7	14
15	8	7	8	8	16

Page 34

1. Ben
2. Anna
3. Mum
4. Dad

Page 35

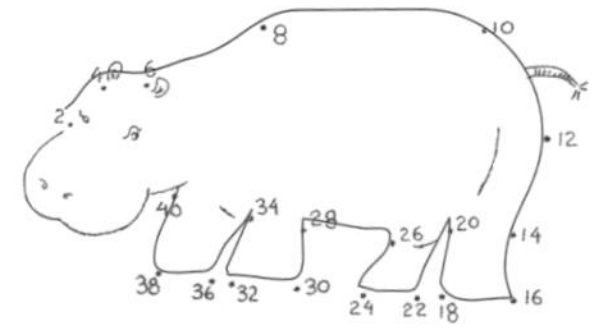

1. fat
2. water
3. grass
4. hippo

Pages 32–33

mountain; tiger; 12; river or stream; porcupine; 5; palm tree; zebra; box or fox; 8; rainbow; anteater; bear or bare; pond; 9; 1; trees or forest; panda; 6; snake; tulip or flower; penguin; block or black; waterfall; sheep

Page 36

1. to the water fountain
2. flag
3. parrot
4. 2, 1, 3
5.

Page 37

5	10	6	22	13	8
11	15	7	18	31	14
17	20	25	32	47	71
36	22	30	35	40	48
51	56	43	33	45	50

Page 38

4.

Page 39

Drawings will vary.

Page 40

Page 41

Riddles will vary.

Page 42

Page 43

1. B
2. E
3. A
4. D
5. C

Page 44

Kinds of animals	Animals we want	Animals we have	How many more do we need?
camel	8	4	4
deer	15	9	6
giraffe	10	7	3
hippo	12	8	4
pig	14	7	7
sheep	18	9	9
buffalo	9	5	4
moose	13	6	7

Page 45

5	12	8	5	10
+8	-6	+2	+7	-3
13	6	10	12	7
-7	+3	-5	-6	+7
6	9	5	6	14
+4	+3	+7	+8	-6
10	12	12	14	8

moose

Page 46

Page 47

1. Yes
2. No
3. No
4. tracks
5. the forest
6. last night

Page 48

2. 20p, 20p, 20p, 20p, 10p; Yes
3. 20p, 20p, 10p, 10p, 10p; Yes
4. 20p, 10p, 10p, 5p, 5p; No

Page 49

1. 20p + 75p = 95p
2. 44p + 50p = 94p
3. 42p + 34p = 76p
4. 35p + 52p = 87p

Page 52

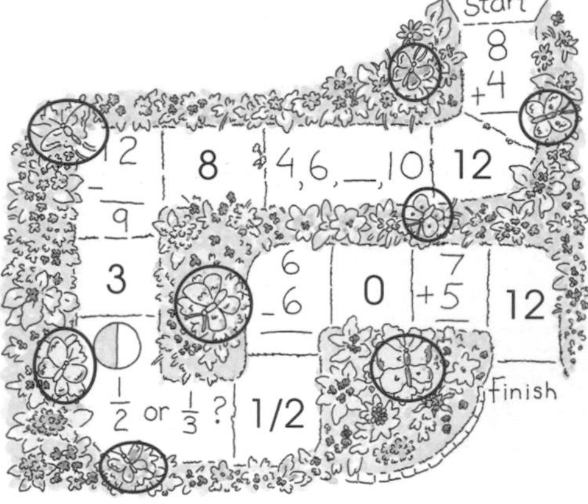

8 butterflies

Page 57

Reasons children like zoos will vary.

Page 50

$\frac{1}{2}$ $\frac{1}{4}$

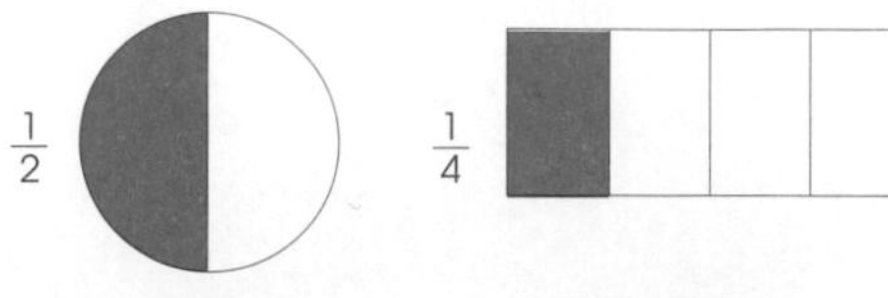

$\frac{1}{3}$

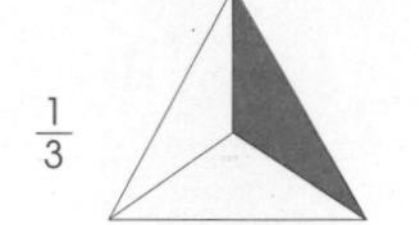

$\frac{2}{2}$

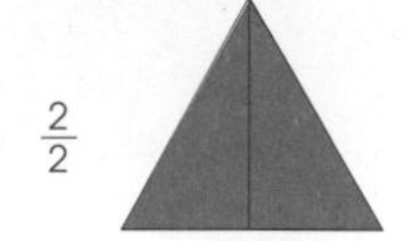

$\frac{3}{4}$

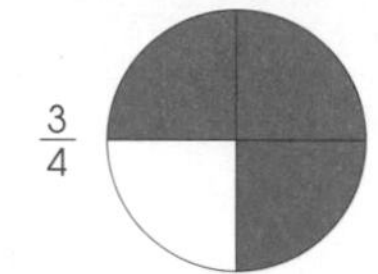

$\frac{2}{3}$

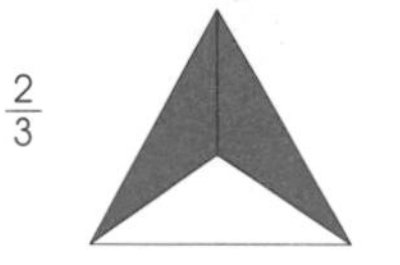

Page 53

Letters will vary but should follow correct letter form.

Pages 54–55

1. long tails
2. short tails
3. Bears' tails changed because Bear froze his tail in the pond and broke it off when he pulled it out of the ice.

Page 51

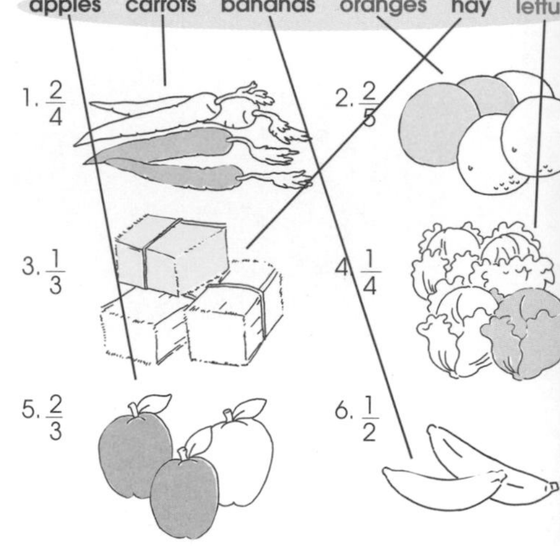

Page 56

Guesses will vary.